Lucy Gray

OR, SOLITUDE

WILLIAM WORDSWORTH illustrated by GILBERT RISWOLD

Prentice-Hall, Inc., Englewood Cliffs, New Jersey

Lucy Gray

OR, SOLITUDE

Lucy Gray or, Solitude by William Wordsworth
illustrated by Gilbert Riswold

© 1964 by Prentice-Hall, Inc., Englewood Cliffs, N. J.
Library of Congress Catalog Card Number: 64-20289
J 54124

Lucy Gray

OR, SOLITUDE

1799

Written at Goslar in Germany.
It was founded on a circumstance
told me by my Sister, of a little girl
who, not far from Halifax in Yorkshire,
was bewildered in a snow - storm.

William Wordsworth

Oft I had heard of Lucy Gray:
And, when I crossed the wild,
I chanced to see at break of day
The solitary child.

No mate, no comrade Lucy knew;
She dwelt on a wide moor,
—The sweetest thing that ever grew
Beside a human door!

You yet may spy the fawn at play,
The hare upon the green;
But the sweet face of Lucy Gray
Will never more be seen.

"To-night will be a stormy night—
You to the town must go:
And take a lantern, Child, to light
Your mother through the snow."

"That, Father! will I gladly do:
'T is scarcely afternoon—
The minster-clock has just struck two,
And yonder is the moon!"

At this the Father raised his hook,
And snapped a faggot-band;
He plied his work;—and Lucy took
The lantern in her hand.

Not blither is the mountain roe:
With many a wanton stroke
Her feet disperse the powdery snow,
That rises up like smoke.

The storm came on before its time:
She wandered up and down;
And many a hill did Lucy climb:
But never reached the town.

The wretched parents all that night
Went shouting far and wide;
But there was neither sound nor sight
To serve them for a guide.

At day-break on a hill they stood
That overlooked the moor;
And thence they saw the bridge of wood,
A furlong from their door.

They wept — and, turning homeward, cried,
"In heaven we all shall meet;"
—When in the snow the mother spied
The print of Lucy's feet.

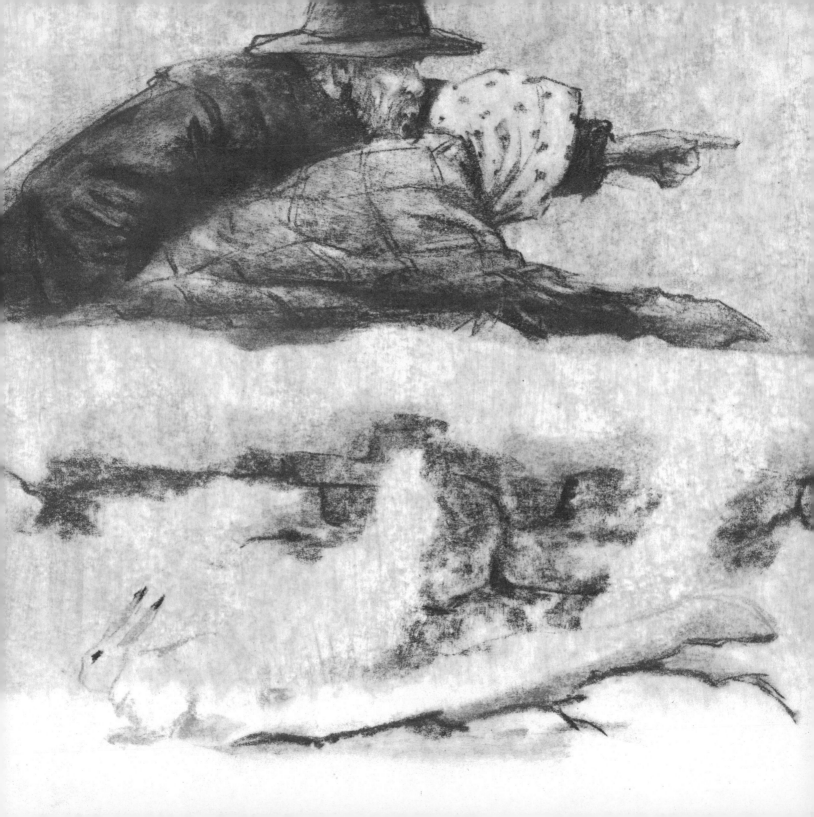

Then downwards from the steep hill's edge
They tracked the footmarks small;
And through the broken hawthorn hedge
And by the long stone-wall;

And then an open field they crossed:
The marks were still the same;
They tracked them on, nor ever lost;
And to the bridge they came.

They followed from the snowy bank,
Those footmarks, one by one,
Into the middle of the plank;
And further there were none!

—Yet some maintain that to this day
She is a living child;
That you may see sweet Lucy Gray
Upon the lonesome wild.

O'er rough and smooth she trips along,
And never looks behind;
And sings a solitary song
That whistles in the wind.

This poem has been hand-lettered by Margaret Riswold